Songs of Pooh
& Christopher Robin

Songs of Pooh & Christopher Robin

CONTENTS

First Published 1984
© Chappell Music Ltd
129 Park Street, London W1Y 3FA

Exclusive Distributors
International Music Publications
60/70 Roden Street, Ilford, England

40-2-14514

It's very, very Funny....

Anxiously

It's ve - ry, ve - ry fun - ny, 'Cos I know I had some hon - ey; 'Cos it had a la - bel on, say - ing HUNNY. A go - lop - tious full - up pot too, And I don't know where it's got to, No, I don't know where it's gone— Well, it's F U N N Y

Isn't it Funny . . . .

Buzzily

Is - n't it fun - ny How a bear likes hon - ey?

Buzz! Buzz! Buzz! I won - der why he does?

It's a ve-ry fun-ny thought that, if Bears were Bees, They'd build their nests at the *bot-tom* of trees. And that be-ing so (if the Bees were Bears) We should-n't have to climb_ up_ all these stairs. _____

How Sweet
to be
a Cloud . . . .

Floatingly

sweet to be a Cloud   Float -ing in the Blue!   Ev'-ry lit-tle cloud——

Al - ways sings a - loud.——   "How   sweet   to   be   a   Cloud

Cottleston Pie

"Cot - tle - ston, Cot - tle - ston, Cot - tle - ston Pie."

Cot - tle - ston,

Cot - tle - ston, Cot - tle - ston Pie. A fish____ can't whis - tle and

neith - er can I. Ask me a rid - dle and I re - ply:

"Cot - tle - ston, Cot - tle - ston, Cot - tle - ston Pie."

Cot - tle - ston, Cot - tle - ston, Cot - tle - ston Pie. Why does a chick - en, I don't__ know why. Ask me a rid - dle and I__ re - ply: "Cot - tle - ston, Cot - tle - ston, Cot - tle - ston Pie!"__

Lines

Written by

a Bear of Very Little Brain

Briskly

On Mon - day, when the sun is hot I

won - der to my - self a lot: "Now is it true, or is it not, That

what is which and which is what?" On Tues-day, when it

hails and snows, The feel - ing on me grows and grows That hard - ly an - y -

-bod - y knows If those are these or these are those.

On Wednes-day, when the

sky is blue, And I have noth-ing else to do, I some-times won - der

if it's true That who is what and what is who.

On Thurs-day, when it starts to freeze And

hoar - frost twink - les on the trees, How ve - ry rea - di - ly one sees That

these are whose— but whose are these?____

On Fri - day— On Fri - day-

(Spoken)

On Fri - day— "What did happen on Friday?"

Sing Ho!
for the Life of a Bear....

With plenty of spirit

Sing Ho! for the life of a Bear! Sing Ho! for the life of a Bear! I don't much mind if it rains or snows, 'Cos I've got a lot of hon-ey on my nice new nose! I don't much care if it snows or thaws, 'Cos I've

got a lot of hon - ey on my nice clean paws! Sing Ho! for a Bear! Sing
Ho! for a Pooh! And I'll have a lit - tle some - thing in an
hour or two! Sing Ho! for a Bear! Sing Ho! for a Pooh! And I'll
have a lit - tle some - thing in an hour or two!

They all
went off
to discover the Pole . . . .

Expeditiously

They

all went off to dis - cov - er the Pole, Owl and Pig - let and Rab - bit and all; It's a

Thing you Dis - cov - er, as I've— been tole By Owl and Pig - let and Rab - bit and all.

Ee - yore, Chris - to - pher Rob - in and Pooh And Rab - bit's re - la - tions

poco cresc.

19

3 Cheers
for Pooh . . . .

Cheers for Pooh! (For Who?) For Pooh— (Why what did he do?) I thought you knew; He saved his friend from a

wet - ting!

3 Cheers for Bear! (For where?) For Bear— He

could-n't swim, But he res-cued him! (He res-cued who?) Oh, lis - ten, do! I am

talk-ing of Pooh— (*Of who?*) Of Pooh! (*I'm sor-ry I keep for-get - ting.*)

Well, Pooh was a Bear of E -

-nor - mous Brain—(*Just say it a-gain!*) Of e - nor - mous brain—(*Of e - nor-mous what?*) Well, he ate a lot, And I

don't know if he could swim or not, But he man-aged to float on a sort of boat (*On a sort of what?*) Well, a .

sort of pot— So now let's give him three hear - ty cheers (*So now let's give him three hear - ty which-es!*) And

hope he'll be with us for years and years, And grow in health and wis-dom and rich-es!

a tempo — *poco rit.* — *a tempo*

cheers for Pooh! *(For who?)* For Pooh— 3 cheers for Bear! *(For where?)* For Bear— 3 cheers for the won-der-ful

Win-nie the Pooh! *(Just tell me, some-bod-y— WHAT DID HE DO?)*

The more it Snows . . . .

24

What shall we do about poor little Tigger?....

Sadly

What shall we do a-bout poor lit-tle Tig-ger? If he nev-er eats no-thing he'll nev-er get big-ger. He does-n't like hon-ey and hay-corns and this-tles Be--cause of the taste and be-cause of the brist-les.

And all the good things which an an - i - mal likes Have the wrong sort of swal-low or too ma - ny spikes. But what-ev - er his weight in pounds, shil - lings and ounc - es, He al - ways seems big - ger be -

-cause of his bounces. _____

bounces.

I could spend
a happy morning...

Consideringly

I could spend a hap-py morn-ing See-ing Roo, I could

spend a hap-py morn-ing Be-ing Pooh. For it does-n't seem to mat-ter, If I

don't get an-y fat-ter (And I *don't* get an-y fat-ter), What I do.

Oh, I like his way of talk-ing, yes, I do. It's the nic-est way of talk-ing Just for two. And a Help-your-self with Rab-bit Tho' it may be-come a hab-it, Is a *pleas-ant* sort of hab-it For a Pooh. I could spend a hap-py morn-ing See-ing Pig-let. And I

could-n't spend a hap-py morn-ing Not see-ing Pig-let. And it

does-n't seem to mat-ter If I don't see Owl and Ee-yore (or any of the others), And I'm

colla voce.

not going to see Owl or Eeyore (or any of the others) Or Chris-to-pher

Rob-in.

a tempo

f

Oh, the Butterflies
are flying....

Happily

Oh, the but-ter-flies are fly-ing, Now the win-ter days are dy-ing, And the

prim-ros-es are try-ing To be seen. And the tur-tle-doves are coo-ing, And the

woods are up and do-ing, For the vi-o-lets are blue-ing, In the

green. ____ Oh, the hon - ey - bees are gumming On their

lit - tle wings, and humming That the summer, which is com - ing, Will be fun. And the

cows are al - most coo - ing, And the tur - tle - doves are moo - ing, Which is

why a Pooh is pooh - ing In the sun. ____ For the

spring is real - ly spring - ing; You can see the sky - lark sing - ing, And the

blue-bells which are ring-ing, Can be heard. And the cuc-koo is-n't coo-ing, But he's

cuck-ing and he's oo-ing, And a Pooh is sim-ply pooh-ing Like a

bird.

a tempo

rall. al fine.

rit.

I lay on my Chest . . . .

Breathlessly

lay on my chest And I thought it best To pre - tend I was hav-ing an

sempre staccato

eve - ning rest; I lay on my tum And I tried to hum But

noth - ing par - tic - u - lar seemed to come. My

face was flat On the floor, and that Is all ve - ry well for an

ac - ro - bat; But it does - n't seem fair To a Friend - ly Bear To

rit.

stif - fen him out with a bask - et - chair._____ And a

If Rabbit was bigger....

If Rab - bit Was big - ger And fat - ter And strong - er, Or

big - ger Than Tig - ger, If Tig - ger was smal - ler, Then Tig - ger's bad hab - it Of

bounc - ing at Rab - bit Would mat - ter No long - er, If Rab - bit Was tal - ler.

This Warm
and Sunny Spot . . .

Sunnily

This warm and sun - ny spot Be - longs to Pooh. And here he won - ders what He's go - ing to do.

Oh, both-er,___ I for-got,_____ Oh,

both-er,___ I for-got,_____

It's Pig - let's too._____ Oh, both - er, I for -

-got It's Pig let's too._____ *(Spoken)* "Sorry, Piglet!"

Here
lies
a
Tree
. . . .

Dramatically

Here lies a tree which Owl (a

bird) Was fond of when it stood on end, And Owl was talk-ing to a friend Called Me (in case you had-n't

more brightly

heard) When something Oo oc-curred. For lo! the wind was blust-er - ous And flat-tened out his fav-'rite

tree; And things looked bad for him and we—Looked bad, I mean, for he and us—I've nev-er known them

poco cresc.

wuss.— Then Pig-let (PIG-LET) thought a thing: "Courage!" he said. There's al-ways

hope. I want a thin-nish piece of rope. Or, if there is-n't an-y, bring A thick-ish piece of

with more spirit

string." So to the let-ter-box he rose, While Pooh and Owl said "Oh!" and "Hum!" And where the let-ters al-ways

come (Called "LETTERS ON-LY") Pig-let sqoze His head and then his toes.—

O gal-lant Pig-let (PIG-LET)! Ho! Did Pig-let trem-ble? Did he blinch? No, no, he strug-gled inch by

inch Through LETTERS ON - LY, as I know Be-cause I saw him go. He ran and ran, and then he

stood And shout-ed, "Help for Owl, a bird, And Pooh, a bear!" un-til he heard The oth-ers com-ing through the

wood As quick-ly as they could. __ "Help-help and Res-cue!" Pig-let cried, And

showed the oth-ers where to go. [Sing ho! for Pig-let (PIG-LET) ho!] And soon the door was o-pened wide,

And we were both out - side! __ Sing ho! for Pig-let, ho! Ho!

Christopher Robin
is going....

Christ-to-pher Rob-in is go-ing. At least I think he

is. Where? No - bod - y knows. But he is go-ing— I mean he

goes (*To rhyme with"knows"*) Do we care? (*To rhyme with "where"*) We

Disobedience

Marching round the nursery

James   James   Mor - ri - son Mo - ri - son Weath - er - by George   Du - pree_____
King   John   Put up a no - tice "LOST   or STOL-EN or   STRAYED!_

Took   great   Care of his Moth - er, Tho' he was on - ly   three._____
James   James   Mor - ri - son's Moth - er Seems to have been   mis - laid._____

James   James   Said to his Moth - er, "Moth - er" he   said, said he;_____   "You must
Last   seen   Wand - er - ing vague - ly: Quite of her own ac - cord,_____   She

nev - er go down to the end of the town, if you don't go down with me."
tried to get down to the end of the town_____ For - ty shill-ings re - ward!"

James   James
James   James

Mor - ri-son's Moth - er Put on a gold - en gown,_____ James James
Mor-ri-son Mor-ri-son (Com-mon-ly known as Jim)_____ Told his

Mor - ri-son's Moth - er Drove to the end of the town._____ James James
Oth - er re - la - tions Not to go bla - ming *him*._____ James James

Mor - ri-son's Moth - er Said to her-self,_ said she:_____ "I can get_ right down to the
Said to his Moth - er, "Moth-er," he said, said he:_____ "You must nev - er go down to the

end of the town and be back in time for tea."____
end of the town, with - out con - sul - ting me."____

James James

Mor - ri - son's Moth - er Has - n't been heard of since.____ King John

Said he was sor - ry, So did the Queen and Prince.____ King John

(Some-bo-dy told me) Said to a man he knew:____ "If people go down to the

Now then very softly

end of the town Well, what can an - y - one do?" J. J

M. M. W. - G. Du P. Took great

C / o his M×××× Though he was on - ly 3.

J. J. Said to his M×××× "M××××," he said, said he: "You-must-

-nev - er - go-down-to - the - end - of - the - town - if - you - don't - go-down-with ME!"

Missing

Wistfully

Has an-y-bod-y seen my mouse?

I o-pened his box for half a min-ute, Just to make sure he was real-ly in it, And while I was look-ing, he jumped out-side! I tried to catch him, I tried, I tried, I think he's some-where a-bout the house. Has an-y-one seen my

mouse? Un-cle John, have you seen my mouse? Just a small sort of mouse, a

dear lit-tle brown one, He came from the coun-try, he was-n't a town one; So he'll feel all lone-ly in a

Lon-don street; Why, what could he pos-si-bly find to eat? He must be somewhere. I'll ask Aunt Rose: Have

you seen a mouse with a wof-fel-ly nose? Oh! some-where a-bout He's

just got out. Has-n't an-y-bod-y seen my mouse?

Halfway Down

Half-way down the stairs Is a stair where I sit: There is-n't an-y o-ther stair

quite like It. I'm not at the bot-tom, I'm not at the top: So

this is the stair where I al-ways stop.

Half-way up the stairs Is-n't up, And is-n't down. It
is-n't in the nur-ser-y, It is-n't in the town; And
all sorts of fun-ny thoughts Run round my head: "It
is-n't real-ly an-y-where! It's some-where else In-stead!"

Slightly slower

It is-n't real-ly an-y-where! It's some-where else in-stead!

Buckingham

Palace

In march time

They're changing guard at Buck-ing-ham Pal-ace

Chris-to-pher Ro-bin went down with Al-ice

Al-ice is mar-ry-ing one of the guard. "A sol-dier's life is ter-ri-ble hard," Says

Al - ice.

They're chang-ing guard at Buck-ing-ham Palace

Al-ice.   They're chang-ing guard at Buck-ing-ham Pal-ace—

Chris-to-pher Rob-in went down with Al-ice.   They've

great big par-ties in-side the grounds. "I would-n't be King for a hun-dred pounds," Says

Al-ice.   They're chang-ing guard at Buck-ing-ham Pal-ace

Chris-to-pher Rob-in went down with Al-ice   A

59

M. & Cº 101

Vespers

A little faster

know that's right. Was - n't it fun in the bath to - night? The

cold's so cold, and the hot's so hot. Oh! *God bless Dad - dy_ I*

Slower again

Quickening

quite for - got. If I o - pen my fing - ers a lit - tle bit more, I can

see Nan - ny's dress - ing - gown on the door. It's a beau - ti - ful blue, but it

Slower

has - n't a hood. Oh! *God bless Nan - ny and make_ her good._*

again quickening

Mine has a hood, and I lie in bed, And pull the hood right o-ver my head, And I shut my eyes, and I curl up small, And no-bod-y knows that I'm there at all. Oh!

A little slower   *Quickening*

Thank you, God, for a love-ly day. And what was the o-ther I had to say? I said "Bless Dad-dy," so what can it be? Oh!

Printed in Great Britain by West Central Printing Co. Ltd., London and Suffolk